1886 Benz

1896 Peugeot

1906 Renault

1916 Perry

1926 Gumdrop

1936 Jaguar

OF THE MOTOR CAR

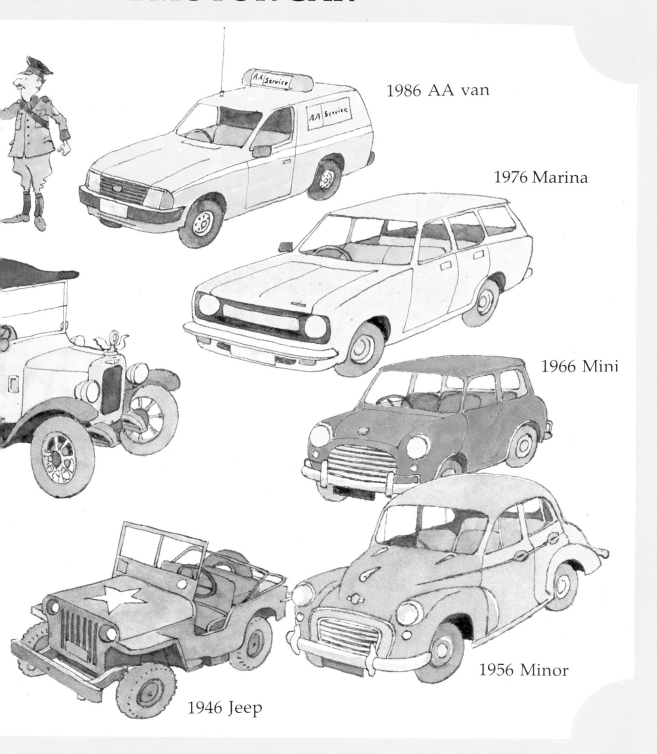

1986 AA van

1976 Marina

1966 Mini

1956 Minor

1946 Jeep

For Mimi, with my love

GUMDROP
TO THE RESCUE

Story and pictures by Val Biro

Puffin Books

ONE FINE DAY Mr Josiah Oldcastle was lying flat on his back.
He was under his car, an Austin Clifton Heavy Twelve-four,
vintage 1926. It was his pride and joy and
he called it Gumdrop.

'Can I help?' enquired his neighbour Mr Bumblebee.
'Not really,' said Mr Oldcastle, 'but a sixty-year
old car needs checking all the time. Tell you what,
though,' he said, scrambling out from under, 'you can
come in and have some tea.' Mr Bumblebee accepted readily.

It was just as well they went into the kitchen, because
Horace the dog was about to help himself to a treacle tart.
'Be off, you horrible hound!' growled Mr Oldcastle as he sat
down. He was worried. Gumdrop had been rattling and
shaking a bit lately and now he knew why. The old
car needed some new parts and Mr Oldcastle had
made a checklist. A long list –
nuts and bolts and screws and
valves, rings and links and
shackle pins. And some
tyres, too!
'But there's no time to get them,'
he said. 'Tomorrow is Gumdrop's
birthday and we are off to the
Beaulieu Historic Motor Show.'
He gave Horace a treacle tart
without thinking.

'Never mind,' said Mr Bumblebee between mouthfuls, 'Gumdrop is a strong car and his old parts will hold until you can replace them.' But Horace felt that he needed some replacements now, so he helped himself to a sausage roll.

Next morning they were ready bright and early and Mr Bumblebee came to see them off. 'Don't go by motorway,' he said, 'it's too dull for a vintage car. Go by this map instead. It is a scenic route from the AA.' He was a member of the Automobile Association and they had worked out a special route for him. But he couldn't go himself after all. Mr Oldcastle was very glad to have the map. 'I would have joined the AA myself, but I'm told that they have no old-fashioned AA badges any more. And Gumdrop couldn't possibly wear a modern one!' He said good-bye, and they drove off, with a merry woof from Horace and a honkety-honk from Gumdrop.

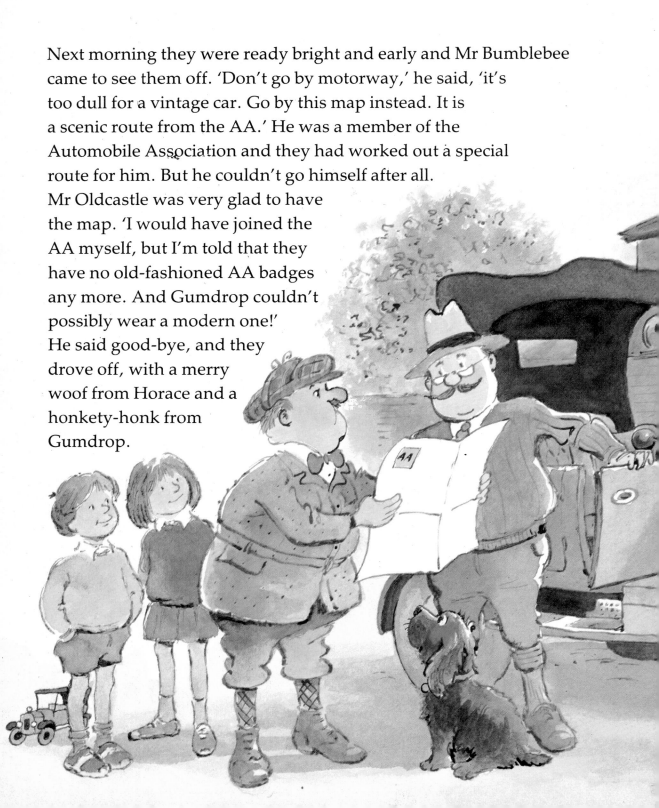

The AA route was so scenic that Mr Oldcastle could hardly
keep his eyes on the road. Down the leafy lanes they went,
among the rolling hills. Cows and birdsong everywhere,
Gumdrop's engine purring sweetly, even if he rattled and
shook from time to time. 'But no matter,' said Mr Oldcastle
and he burst into song himself.

Round a bend he saw a man thumbing a lift. He was dressed like an old-fashioned AA patrol, so naturally Mr Oldcastle stopped. 'May I assist you in any way?' he enquired.

'Oh yes!' cried the man who looked most upset. 'My name is Letts and I was driving my vintage AA motor-cycle when two ruffians jumped out from the trees and, would you believe, stole it without so much as a by-your-leave!'

'We can't have that!' growled Mr Oldcastle. 'Come on, jump in!' And he put his foot down.

Gumdrop shot forward, skidding and lurching round the narrow bends and his old parts rattled and shook more and more. Horace barked, Mr Letts waved his arms and Mr Oldcastle roared mightily, 'Gumdrop to the rescue!'

And there was the motorbike ahead.

With a final burst of speed Gumdrop overtook the bike and
Mr Oldcastle slammed on the brakes. Gumdrop skidded
sideways and came to a screeching halt, blocking the road.
So the motorbike had to stop as well.
Mr Letts jumped out of Gumdrop, but
Horace was even quicker. He leapt
at the ruffians with such
horrible snarling growls
that they were off that
bike in a flash – and
without so much as a
beg-pardon they bolted
for the trees and
vanished.

Whew! The motorbike was safe. It was the earliest AA road
service outfit in existence, and very valuable. Luckily it
was undamaged and Mr Letts was most
grateful. 'I hope I may repay your
valiant rescue,' he said, 'but now
I must get to Beaulieu in time.'
So he got on his bike and with
a wave he phut-phutted away.

Mr Oldcastle followed more slowly. All that speeding
had done no good at all and Gumdrop rattled and
shook more than ever now. 'At least we are on the right
road,' muttered Mr Oldcastle when he saw
a yellow AA sign, 'but I doubt if poor
old Gumdrop will make it.' Just as he
said that, there was an extra loud
rattle, Gumdrop shook violently,
and stopped.
'We've broken down!' he sighed.

'Can I help?' asked a man leaning over the gate.

He was Farmer Dean and he came over to look at Gumdrop's
engine. 'And I shall look under,' said Mr Oldcastle
as he got out and lay flat on his back again. They
checked everything, but there was nothing wrong
with the nuts or bolts or screws or valves,
nor the rings or links or shackle pins.
'We need help,' they said at last,
but there wasn't a garage for
miles. 'I know!' exclaimed
Farmer Dean, who was a member
of the AA, 'I'll call them
from the phone down the road!'
And the AA told him that
they'd come at once.

Sure enough their van arrived in no time. They always come to rescue their members in trouble. 'But you are not a member,' said the patrol sternly to Mr Oldcastle, 'so I fear we can't help.' Then he looked at Gumdrop and his face lit up.

'Why, this is Gumdrop! My children know all about him!' He knew that they'd never forgive him if he didn't help their favourite car. So he decided to make an exception and after a brief examination he soon found the trouble.
'It's your clutch,' he announced. 'The three thrust arms are broken.' But not even his well-equipped yellow AA van had such things as vintage Austin thrust arms.

'Just the same we will get you there in time,' he said and got out his radio. 'This is most irregular, but I am calling for a relay transporter. We can't leave poor old Gumdrop here or let him miss the Show!'

Sure enough the transporter arrived in no time, and Gumdrop was carefully winched up and secured. And so it was that with the AA's help he went piggy-back all the way to the Beaulieu Historic Motor Show.

He got there just in time to be lined up with all the other cars in front of Lord Montagu's great house. The Show was to celebrate the hundredth year of the motorcar, and it included the very first car ever made, the 1886 Benz. There was one for every tenth year, and splendid cars they were too. But none more so than the 1926 Austin Clifton Heavy Twelve-four – despite his broken clutch!

1936   1946   1956   1966   1976   1980

Mr Letts drew up on his motorbike and Mr Oldcastle told him
about the clutch. 'My dear sir,' smiled Mr Letts, 'this bike
is filled with vintage parts and I shall be delighted to help
you in return for your noble rescue.'

He found the thrust arms in his bike and got down to work straight away. He was an expert engineer, and with the help of other AA patrols he fitted the spare parts in no time at all.

Horace was getting hungry by then, and he wished there had been some spare parts for him too. Such as treacle tarts or sausage rolls.

At four o'clock Mr Letts made a speech. He was a
Very Important Member of the AA, and his old bike
had belonged to his grandfather who founded
the AA in 1905. He spoke about the ruffians
who tried to steal his bike. 'It was
Gumdrop who came to the rescue,' he
said, 'and for that valiant act I
shall propose him to be elected
as an honorary member of the
Automobile Association.'

Then Lord Montagu himself made a speech. 'This is Gumdrop's sixtieth birthday, and now that he is a member of the AA let me present him with this suitably old-fashioned AA brass badge!' Mr Oldcastle was very proud of Gumdrop and patted him on the bonnet. The other drivers cheered and they all gave Gumdrop some birthday presents too.

When Mr Oldcastle got home and opened them, you can imagine how delighted he was, not to mention Horace the dog! For on that memorable day they were given so many presents that it felt just like Christmas!

Here is the list:

Twelve treacle tarts

Eleven engine bolts

Ten tappet screws

Nine new nuts

Eight exhaust valves

Seven shackle pins

Six sausage rolls

Five felt rings

Four brake links

Three thrust arms

Two tyres

and an old-fashioned
AA brass badge.

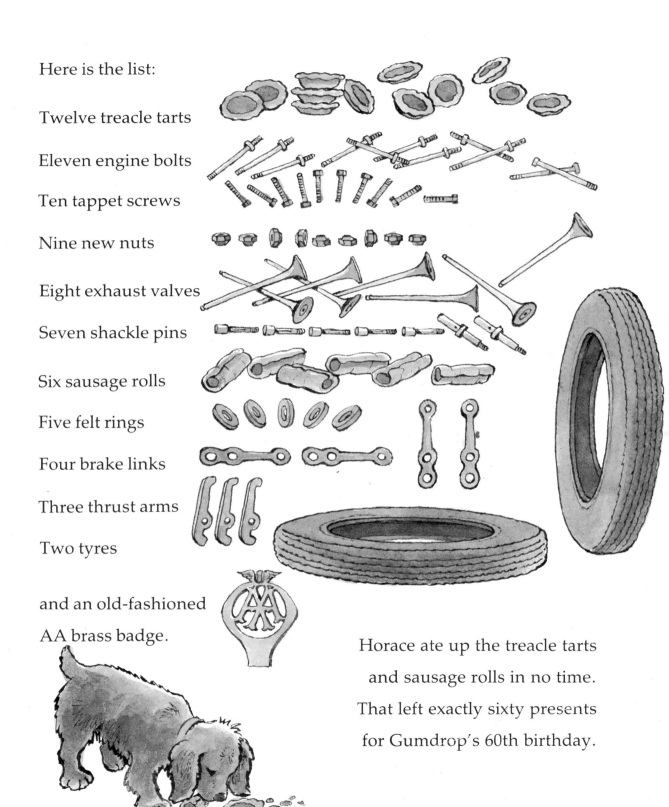

Horace ate up the treacle tarts
and sausage rolls in no time.
That left exactly sixty presents
for Gumdrop's 60th birthday.

All the new parts have now been fitted and
Gumdrop doesn't rattle or shake any more.
And if ever he broke down again, he knows
that the AA would come to the rescue.
Honkety Honk!